BEST EVER
FAT FREE
COOKBOOK